The Super Easy
Carnivore Diet
for Beginners

1500 Days of Quick and Satisfying Recipes to Navigate the Meaty Diet| Full Color Edition

Jessica G. Snider

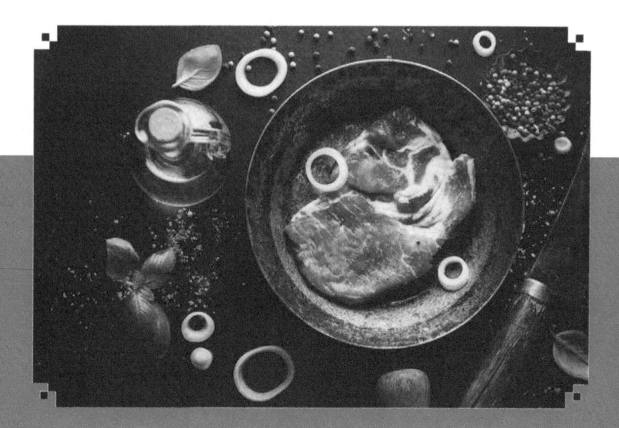

Editor: AALIYAH LYONS

Interior Design: BROOKE WHITE

Cover Art: DANIELLE REES

Food stylist: SIENNA ADAMS

Table Of Contents

Introduction	1	Smoked Sea Salt	15
		Salted Beef Stock	16
Chapter 1		Tahini Sauce	16
Understanding the Carnivore Diet	2	Chicken Stock	17
Principles of the Carnivore Diet	3	Scrambled Eggs and Cream	17
Implementing a Carnivore	4	Seafood Stock	18
Diet	4	Italian Vinaigrette	18
Essentials of Carnivore Cooking	6	Salt-Cured Egg Yolks	19
		Teriyaki Sauce	19
Chapter 2		Chicken Bone Broth	20
4-Week Meal Plan	9	Homemade Butter	20
Week 1	10		
Week 2	10	**Chapter 4**	
Week 3	11	**Breakfast Bonanza**	21
Week 4	12	Carnivore Egg Cups	22
		Bacon and Feta Omelet	22
Chapter 3		Ham Hocks and Fried Eggs	23
Culinary Basics	14	Tuna Salad Deviled Eggs	23
Scotch Eggs	15	Bacon, Egg, and Cheese Cups	24

Scrambled Eggs in a Mug	24	Grilled Mediterranean Lamb Chops	45
Sausage Cakes with Poached Eggs	25	Smoked Beef Roast	45
Chorizo Sausage Egg Cakes	25		
Classic Eggs with Canadian Bacon	26	**Chapter 8**	
Ham Cheese Egg Cups	26	**Pork Parade**	46
		Sous Vide Pork Chop	47
Chapter 5		Curried Pork Skewers	47
Snack Attack and Appetizers	27	Baked Balsamic-Glazed Pork Tenderloin	48
Smoked Salmon Deviled Eggs	28	Hot Pork Meatballs	48
Beef Jerky	28	Chili-Spiced Ribs	49
Pig Candy	29	Shredded Pork Butt Roast	49
Ranch and Blue Cheese Dip	29	Pork Rind Waffles	50
Crispy Chicken Nuggets	30	Bacon Buck Burgers	50
Cheesy Chicken Dip	30		
Pesto Cheese Dip	31	**Chapter 9**	
Camembert & Chili Bacon Balls	31	**Poultry Picks**	51
Carnivore Frosting	32	Braised Rabbit	52
Creamy Chicken Dip	32	Feta & Mozzarella Chicken	52
		Grilled Wild Duck Breast	53
Chapter 6		Roasted Chicken with Creamy Topping	53
Salads, Sides, and More	33	Moroccan Roast Chicken	54
Corned Lamb Hearts	34	Thyme Chicken Thighs	54
Chicken Wings	34	Grilled Huli Huli Chicken	55
Classic Hot Chicken Drumettes	35	Marinated Fried Chicken	55
The Real Meat-Lover's Pizza	35		
Beef Heart Recipe	36	**Chapter 10**	
Chipotle Shrimp Cakes	36	**Seafood Splendor**	56
Creamed Monkfish Salad	37	Codfish Nuggets	57
Ranch Bacon Chips	37	Salmon with Herb Cream Sauce	57
Chicken Liver Pate	38	Grilled Salmon	58
Sautéed Beef Kidney	38	Poached Scallops	58
		Bacon-Wrapped Scallops	59
Chapter 7		Dill Potted Salmon	59
Beef and Lamb Extravaganza	39	Lobster Roll In A Bowl	60
Baked Lamb and Feta Patties	40	Broiled Honey Sesame Shrimp	60
Grilled Lamb Kofta	40	Garlic-and-Herb-Roasted Sardines	61
Grilled Beef Short Loin	41	Crispy Baked Fish Sticks	61
Oven-Roasted Beef Brisket	41		
Swedish Roast Beef	42	**Appendix 1 Measurement Conversion**	
Zesty Grilled Ham	42	**Chart**	62
BBQ Beef Short Ribs	43	**Appendix 2 The Dirty Dozen and Clean**	
Awesome Beef Cheeseburgers	43	**Fifteen**	63
Stuffed Lamb Shoulder	44	**Appendix 3 Index**	64
Beef Heart and Liver Meatballs	44		

Introduction

In a world inundated with dietary advice, where every new fad promises health and vitality, there's a simplicity that beckons—a primal instinct buried deep within us, waiting to be awakened. Welcome to the Carnivore Diet, a journey back to our roots, where sustenance is found in the purest form: the nourishing bounty of the animal kingdom.

Amidst the noise of modern nutrition, the Carnivore Diet stands as a testament to the enduring wisdom of our ancestors. It strips away the complexities of contemporary eating habits, inviting us to rediscover the fundamental connection between food and vitality. In a culture overrun with processed foods and dietary dogmas, the Carnivore Diet offers a return to simplicity—a return to the nourishing essence of real, whole foods.

As you flip through these pages, you'll encounter an array of tantalizing recipes meticulously crafted to satisfy both your palate and your primal instincts. From succulent steaks to sizzling bacon-wrapped delicacies, each dish has been thoughtfully curated to showcase the richness and diversity of the Carnivore Diet. But beyond the sheer indulgence of flavors, these recipes serve as a testament to the remarkable versatility and nutritional prowess of animal-based foods.

But this cookbook is more than just a collection of recipes—it's a celebration of a lifestyle rooted in simplicity, sustainability, and self-discovery. It's a reminder that optimal health and well-being are within reach when we align ourselves with the wisdom of our ancestors and embrace the nourishing power of real, wholesome foods.

Whether you're a seasoned carnivore or a curious newcomer, this cookbook offers something for everyone. So, sharpen your knives, fire up the grill, and prepare to embark on a culinary adventure like no other. Let these recipes be your guide as you reclaim your primal roots and unleash the boundless potential of the Carnivore Diet.

Here's to savoring every bite and embracing the primal within us all.

Chapter 1

Understanding the Carnivore Diet

Principles of the Carnivore Diet

The Carnivore Diet, an eating pattern centered around consuming only animal products, has gained significant attention in recent years. Despite its current popularity, the diet has historical roots and is often viewed through evolutionary perspectives on human nutrition. This article explores the historical context, evolutionary perspectives, the definition of eating carnivore, and the science behind the Carnivore Diet.

HISTORICAL CONTEXT

The idea of an all-meat diet isn't new. Historical records show that various cultures, such as the Inuit in the Arctic and certain Native American tribes, subsisted primarily on animal products for extended periods. These communities thrived on diets rich in animal fats and proteins, challenging the notion that humans require a diverse range of foods for optimal health.

In the modern era, the Carnivore Diet gained traction through individuals like Dr. Shawn Baker and Dr. Paul Saladino, who advocate for its benefits based on personal experience and limited scientific evidence. Despite criticism and skepticism from mainstream nutritionists, the diet has attracted a devoted following, with anecdotal reports of weight loss, improved energy levels, and better overall health.

EVOLUTIONARY PERSPECTIVES ON HUMAN NUTRITION

Evolutionary perspectives suggest that humans evolved as hunters and gatherers, primarily consuming animal flesh and plant foods when available. Proponents of the Carnivore Diet argue that our ancestors thrived on animal-based diets for millions of years before the advent of agriculture introduced grains and other plant foods into the human diet.

According to evolutionary biologists, our genetic makeup is adapted to metabolize and derive nutrients efficiently from animal products. They argue that the shift towards a diet heavy in processed foods and carbohydrates may be at odds with our evolutionary history, contributing to modern health issues like obesity, diabetes, and cardiovascular disease.

THE DEFINITION OF EATING CARNIVORE

The Carnivore Diet is straightforward in its prescription: eat only animal products, including meat, fish, eggs, and certain dairy products like cheese and butter. This means eliminating all plant-based foods, including fruits, vegetables, grains, legumes, and processed foods from the diet.

Advocates of the diet often emphasize the importance of sourcing high-quality animal products, preferably from pasture-raised or wild-caught animals. They believe that the nutritional profile of these foods is superior to conventionally raised animal products and may offer additional health benefits.

THE SCIENCE BEHIND THE CARNIVORE DIET

While the Carnivore Diet lacks extensive scientific research compared to more mainstream dietary approaches, some studies and anecdotal evidence support its potential benefits.

NUTRITIONAL COMPOSITION

Animal products are rich sources of essential nutrients like protein, vitamins (such as B12 and D), minerals (including iron and zinc), and healthy fats (like omega-3 fatty acids). A well-planned Carnivore Diet can provide all the necessary nutrients for optimal health.

WEIGHT LOSS

Some individuals report significant weight loss on the Carnivore Diet, attributing it to reduced calorie intake, improved satiety, and metabolic changes associated with ketosis—a metabolic state where the body burns fat for fuel.

IMPROVED METABOLIC HEALTH

Preliminary studies suggest that low-carbohydrate, high-fat diets, like the Carnivore Diet, may improve markers of metabolic health, including blood sugar levels, insulin sensitivity, and cholesterol profiles.

GUT HEALTH

One of the controversial aspects of the Carnivore Diet is its potential impact on gut health. While proponents claim relief from digestive issues like bloating and gas, critics argue that eliminating fiber-rich plant foods may disrupt the gut microbiota and increase the risk of long-term gastrointestinal problems. Further research is necessary to understand the implications for gut health fully.

Implementing a Carnivore Diet

TRANSITIONING TO THE CARNIVORE DIET

Transitioning to the Carnivore Diet requires careful planning and consideration to ensure a smooth adjustment while addressing common misconceptions. This guide outlines practical steps to help individuals transition to the Carnivore Diet effectively.

EDUCATE YOURSELF

Before starting the Carnivore Diet, educate yourself about its principles, potential benefits, and risks. Familiarize yourself with the types of foods allowed and excluded on the diet, as well as any potential nutrient deficiencies that may arise.

Gradual Reduction of Non-Carnivore Foods Instead of immediately eliminating all non-carnivore foods from your diet, consider gradually reducing them over time. Begin by eliminating processed foods, grains, and sugar, then gradually reduce fruits, vegetables, and other plant-based foods.

EMPHASIZE ANIMAL PRODUCTS

Focus on incorporating a variety of animal products into your meals, including beef, pork, poultry, fish, eggs, and dairy (if tolerated). Opt for high-quality, pasture-raised, and organic options whenever possible to maximize nutrient intake.

EXPERIMENT WITH DIFFERENT CUTS AND COOKING METHODS

Explore different cuts of meat and cooking methods to keep your meals interesting and enjoyable. Experiment with grilling, roasting, stewing, and slow-cooking to enhance flavor and texture.

MONITOR YOUR BODY'S RESPONSE

Pay attention to how your body responds to the transition. Some individuals may experience temporary symptoms like fatigue, headaches, or digestive discomfort as their bodies adjust to the new diet. Keep a food diary to track your meals and any associated symptoms.

STAY HYDRATED

Drink plenty of water to stay hydrated, especially during the transition period. While the Carnivore Diet eliminates many sources of dietary water, meat and other animal products still contain water, and adequate hydration is crucial for overall health.

CONSIDER ELECTROLYTE SUPPLEMENTATION

As your body adjusts to the Carnivore Diet, you may experience changes in electrolyte balance, leading to symptoms like fatigue, muscle cramps, or headaches. Consider supplementing with electrolytes like sodium, potassium, and magnesium to support optimal hydration and electrolyte balance.

MONITOR NUTRIENT INTAKE

Ensure you're meeting your nutritional needs by monitoring your intake of essential nutrients like protein, vitamins (especially B12 and D), minerals (such as iron and zinc), and healthy fats.

ADDRESSING COMMON MISCONCEPTIONS

NUTRIENT DEFICIENCIES

One of the most prevalent misconceptions surrounding the Carnivore Diet is the concern about potential nutrient deficiencies due to the exclusion of plant-based foods. Critics often argue that eliminating fruits, vegetables, and grains may lead to deficiencies in essential vitamins, minerals,

and fiber. However, proponents of the Carnivore Diet emphasize that animal products are highly nutritious, containing ample amounts of protein, vitamins (such as B12 and D), minerals (like iron and zinc), and healthy fats. With careful planning and a diverse selection of animal products, individuals can meet their nutritional needs without reliance on plant foods. Additionally, supplementation may be utilized to address any potential deficiencies, ensuring overall nutritional adequacy on the Carnivore Diet.

GUT HEALTH CONCERNS

Another misconception pertains to the impact of the Carnivore Diet on gut health. Skeptics argue that the lack of dietary fiber from plant foods may disrupt the balance of gut microbiota and lead to digestive issues. While it is true that fiber plays a role in promoting gut health and regularity, proponents of the Carnivore Diet contend that the human body can adapt to a fiber-free diet. Moreover, anecdotal reports suggest that some individuals experience improvements in digestive symptoms like bloating and gas upon adopting the Carnivore Diet. Nevertheless, further research is warranted to elucidate the long-term effects of the Carnivore Diet on gut microbiota composition and digestive function.

SUSTAINABILITY CONCERNS

Critics often raise concerns about the sustainability of the Carnivore Diet, questioning its environmental impact and long-term feasibility. The perception that meat production contributes significantly to greenhouse gas emissions and environmental degradation fuels skepticism about the diet's sustainability. However, proponents argue that sourcing high-quality, pasture-raised, and sustainably produced animal products can mitigate environmental concerns associated with conventional meat production. Additionally, the Carnivore Diet's simplicity and emphasis on whole foods make it a potentially sustainable dietary approach for individuals seeking to minimize their environmental footprint while optimizing their health.

LONG-TERM HEALTH RISKS

Finally, there are concerns about the potential long-term health risks associated with the Carnivore Diet, including cardiovascular disease, kidney issues, and cancer. Critics argue that the high intake of animal products, particularly red meat, may increase the risk of chronic diseases. However, existing research on the health effects of red meat consumption is mixed, with some studies suggesting potential associations with adverse health outcomes and others finding no significant correlation. Proponents of the Carnivore Diet highlight the diet's potential benefits for weight management, metabolic health, and inflammation reduction but acknowledge the need for further research to fully understand its long-term implications.

Essentials of Carnivore Cooking

SAVVY MEAT SELECTION

Selecting the right meat is crucial for a successful Carnivore Diet. Understanding the various meat varieties, their nutritional profiles, and how to choose high-quality cuts can enhance your dining experience and optimize your health. This guide unveils the secrets of meat selection, providing essential tips for savvy carnivores.

UNDERSTANDING MEAT VARIETIES

Meat comes in various forms, each offering unique flavors, textures, and nutritional benefits. Here are some common meat varieties to consider:

- Beef: Beef is a versatile meat option rich in protein, iron, zinc, and B vitamins. Different cuts offer varying levels of fat content and tenderness. Popular beef cuts include ribeye, sirloin, flank steak, and ground beef.
- Pork: Pork is known for its rich flavor and tender texture. It provides essential nutrients like protein, B vitamins, and minerals. Common pork cuts include pork chops, tenderloin, ribs, and bacon.
- Poultry: Poultry, such as chicken and turkey, is a lean source of protein with relatively low fat content. It also contains essential vitamins and minerals like niacin, phosphorus, and selenium. Choose skin-on poultry for added flavor and moisture.
- Fish and Seafood: Fish and seafood are excellent sources of omega-3 fatty acids, protein, and various vitamins and minerals. Opt for fatty fish like salmon, mackerel, and sardines for maximum omega-3 content. Other seafood options include shrimp, scallops, and shellfish.

TIPS FOR SELECTING HIGH-QUALITY MEAT

When purchasing meat, consider the following tips to ensure you're getting the highest quality:

- Look for Freshness: Choose meats that are

bright in color, firm to the touch, and free from any unpleasant odors. Avoid meat with excessive discoloration or signs of spoilage.

- Check Marbling: Marbling refers to the intramuscular fat within the meat, which enhances flavor and tenderness. Look for cuts with visible marbling for a juicier and more flavorful eating experience.
- Consider Source and Production Methods: Whenever possible, opt for meats that are pasture-raised, grass-fed, organic, or sustainably sourced. These options tend to be higher in nutrients and free from antibiotics, hormones, and other additives.
- Inspect Packaging: Check the packaging for any leaks, tears, or damage that could indicate improper handling or storage. Vacuum-sealed packaging helps maintain freshness and prevent contamination.

ESSENTIAL CARNIVORE KITCHEN TOOLS

Equipping your kitchen with the right tools can make meat preparation and cooking more efficient and enjoyable. Here are some essential tools for carnivores:

- Quality Knives: Invest in a set of high-quality knives for slicing, dicing, and chopping meat with precision. A sharp chef's knife, boning knife, and utility knife are essential for various cutting tasks.
- Meat Thermometer: A meat thermometer ensures that your meat is cooked to the desired level of doneness, preventing overcooking or undercooking. Choose a digital thermometer for accurate and quick readings.
- Cast Iron Skillet: A cast iron skillet is ideal for searing, sautéing, and frying meat to perfection. It retains heat well and develops a natural non-stick surface over time, making it a versatile tool for carnivore cooking.
- Grill or Smoker: Grilling or smoking meat adds depth of flavor and enhances its natural juiciness. Invest in a quality grill or smoker for outdoor cooking experiences and delicious barbecue creations.
- Meat Tenderizer: A meat tenderizer helps break down tough muscle fibers, resulting in more tender and flavorful meat. Choose from mallet-style tenderizers or mechanical options with sharp blades.

PERFECTING THE ART OF MEAT COOKERY

Cooking meat to perfection requires skill, technique, and attention to detail. Here are some tips for mastering the art of meat cookery:

- Seasoning: Enhance the flavor of meat with simple seasonings like salt, pepper, herbs, and spices. Experiment with different flavor combinations to elevate your dishes.
- Searing: Searing meat at high temperatures creates a caramelized crust, locking in moisture and flavor. Preheat your cooking surface thoroughly and sear meat until golden brown on all sides before finishing in the oven or on the grill.
- Resting: Allow cooked meat to rest for a few minutes before slicing or serving to allow the juices to redistribute evenly. Tent the meat loosely with foil to keep it warm while resting.
- Doneness: Use a meat thermometer to determine the doneness of meat accurately. Refer to USDA guidelines for safe internal temperatures for different types of meat.

- Experimentation: Don't be afraid to experiment with different cooking methods, temperatures, and cuts of meat. Embrace trial and error to discover your preferred cooking techniques and flavor profiles.

In essence, the Carnivore Diet offers a tantalizing journey into the realm of metabolic efficiency and nutritional optimization. With its roots firmly grounded in evolutionary science and the tantalizing promise of weight management, metabolic health, and reduced inflammation, this dietary approach beckons adventurous souls seeking a transformative path to well-being. However, as with any profound dietary shift, caution and informed decision-making are paramount. By delving into the fascinating science underpinning the Carnivore Diet and consulting with healthcare professionals, individuals can embark on a thrilling odyssey towards better health and vitality, one succulent steak at a time. Embrace the adventure, and unlock the potential of the Carnivore Diet for a brighter, healthier tomorrow.

Chapter 2

4-Week Meal Plan

Week 1

DAY 1:
- Breakfast: Ham Hocks and Fried Eggs
- Lunch: Baked Lamb and Feta Patties
- Snack: Ranch and Blue Cheese Dip
- Dinner: Pork Rind Waffles

Total for the day:
Calories: 1277 ; Fat: 96.1 g; Protein: 87 g; Carbs: 7.7 g

DAY 2:
- Breakfast: Ham Hocks and Fried Eggs
- Lunch: Baked Lamb and Feta Patties
- Snack: Ranch and Blue Cheese Dip
- Dinner: Pork Rind Waffles

Total for the day:
Calories: 1277 ; Fat: 96.1 g; Protein: 87 g; Carbs: 7.7 g

DAY 3:
- Breakfast: Ham Hocks and Fried Eggs
- Lunch: Baked Lamb and Feta Patties
- Snack: Ranch and Blue Cheese Dip
- Dinner: Pork Rind Waffles

Total for the day:
Calories: 1277 ; Fat: 96.1 g; Protein: 87 g; Carbs: 7.7 g

DAY 4:
- Breakfast: Ham Hocks and Fried Eggs
- Lunch: Baked Lamb and Feta Patties
- Snack: Ranch and Blue Cheese Dip
- Dinner: Pork Rind Waffles

Total for the day:
Calories: 1277 ; Fat: 96.1 g; Protein: 87 g; Carbs: 7.7 g

DAY 5:
- Breakfast: Classic Eggs with Canadian Bacon

- Lunch: Baked Lamb and Feta Patties
- Snack: Ranch and Blue Cheese Dip
- Dinner: Pork Rind Waffles

Total for the day:
Calories: 1141; Fat: 72.4 g; Protein: 73 g; Carbs: 12.5 g

DAY 6:
- Breakfast: Classic Eggs with Canadian Bacon
- Lunch: Baked Lamb and Feta Patties
- Snack: Ranch and Blue Cheese Dip
- Dinner: Pork Rind Waffles

Total for the day:
Calories: 1141; Fat: 72.4 g; Protein: 73 g; Carbs: 12.5 g

DAY 7:
- Breakfast: Classic Eggs with Canadian Bacon
- Lunch: Pork Rind Waffles
- Snack: Ranch and Blue Cheese Dip
- Dinner: Pork Rind Waffles

Total for the day:
Calories: 1208; Fat: 73.4 g; Protein: 86 g; Carb;s: 16.5 g

Week 2

DAY 1:
- Breakfast: Tuna Salad Deviled Eggs
- Lunch: Swedish Roast Beef
- Snack: Pesto Cheese Dip
- Dinner: Marinated Fried Chicken

Total for the day:
Calories: 963; Fat: 45.9 g; Protein: 85.3 g; Carbs: 13 g

DAY 2:
- Breakfast: Tuna Salad Deviled Eggs

- Lunch: Swedish Roast Beef
- Snack: Pesto Cheese Dip
- Dinner: Marinated Fried Chicken

Total for the day:
Calories: 963; Fat: 45.9 g; Protein: 85.3 g; Carbs: 13 g

DAY 3:
- Breakfast: Tuna Salad Deviled Eggs
- Lunch: Swedish Roast Beef
- Snack: Pesto Cheese Dip
- Dinner: Marinated Fried Chicken

Total for the day:
- **Calories: 963; Fat: 45.9 g; Protein: 85.3 g; Carbs: 13 g**

DAY 4:
- Breakfast: Tuna Salad Deviled Eggs
- Lunch: Swedish Roast Beef
- Snack: Pesto Cheese Dip
- Dinner: Marinated Fried Chicken

Total for the day:
Calories: 963; Fat: 45.9 g; Protein: 85.3 g; Carbs: 13 g

DAY 5:
- Breakfast: Chorizo Sausage Egg Cakes
- Lunch: Swedish Roast Beef
- Snack: Pesto Cheese Dip
- Dinner: Sweet-and-Sour Duck Legs

Total for the day:
Calories: 1254; Fat: 76.1 g; Protein: 115 g; Carbs: 23 g

DAY 6:
- Breakfast: Chorizo Sausage Egg Cakes
- Lunch: Swedish Roast Beef
- Snack: Pesto Cheese Dip
- Dinner: Sweet-and-Sour Duck Legs

Total for the day:
Calories: 1254; Fat: 76.1 g; Protein: 115 g; Carbs: 23 g

DAY 7:
- Breakfast: Chorizo Sausage Egg Cakes
- Lunch: Swedish Roast Beef
- Snack: Pesto Cheese Dip
- Dinner: Swedish Roast Beef

Total for the day:
Calories: 1316; Fat: 74.1 g; Protein: 188 g; Carbs: 19 g

Week 3

DAY 1:
- Breakfast: Ham Cheese Egg Cups
- Lunch: Smoked Beef Roast
- Snack: Chicken Wings
- Dinner: Smoked Beef Roast

Total for the day:
Calories: 1476; Fat: 96.6 g; Protein: 140 g; Carbs: 1.8 g

DAY 2:
- Breakfast: Ham Cheese Egg Cups
- Lunch: Smoked Beef Roast
- Snack: Chicken Wings
- Dinner: Smoked Beef Roast

Total for the day:
Calories: 1476; Fat: 96.6 g; Protein: 140 g; Carbs: 1.8 g

DAY 3:
- Breakfast: Ham Cheese Egg Cups
- Lunch: Smoked Beef Roast
- Snack: Chicken Wings
- Dinner: Smoked Beef Roast

Total for the day:
Calories: 1476; Fat: 96.6 g; Protein: 140 g; Carbs: 1.8 g

DAY 4:

- Breakfast: Ham Cheese Egg Cups
- Lunch: Smoked Beef Roast
- Snack: Chicken Wings
- Dinner: Smoked Beef Roast

Total for the day:
Calories: 1476; Fat: 96.6 g; Protein: 140 g; Carbs: 1.8 g

DAY 5:

- Breakfast: Ham Cheese Egg Cups
- Lunch: Smoked Beef Roast
- Snack: Corned Lamb Hearts
- Dinner: Smoked Beef Roast

Total for the day:
Calories: 1331; Fat: 82.6 g; Protein: 135 g; Carbs: 3.8 g

DAY 6:

- Breakfast: Ham Cheese Egg Cups
- Lunch: Smoked Beef Roast
- Snack: Corned Lamb Hearts
- Dinner: Salmon with Herb Cream Sauce

Total for the day:
Calories: 1292 ; Fat: 89.6 g; Protein: 108 g; Carbs: 5.3 g

DAY 7:

- Breakfast: Ham Cheese Egg Cups
- Lunch: Smoked Beef Roast
- Snack: Corned Lamb Hearts
- Dinner: Salmon with Herb Cream Sauce

Total for the day:
Calories: 1292 ; Fat: 89.6 g; Protein: 108 g; Carbs: 5.3 g

Week 4

DAY 1:

- Breakfast: Carnivore Egg Cups

- Lunch: Oven-Roasted Beef Brisket
- Snack: Beef Jerky
- Dinner: Grilled Wild Duck Breast

Total for the day:
Calories: 1425 ;Fat: 96 g; Protein: 140 g; Carbs: 26 g

DAY 2:

- Breakfast: Carnivore Egg Cups
- Lunch: Oven-Roasted Beef Brisket
- Snack: Beef Jerky
- Dinner: Grilled Wild Duck Breast

Total for the day:
Calories: 1425 ;Fat: 96 g; Protein: 140 g; Carbs: 26 g

DAY 3:

- Breakfast: Carnivore Egg Cups
- Lunch: Oven-Roasted Beef Brisket
- Snack: Beef Jerky
- Dinner: Grilled Wild Duck Breast

Total for the day:
Calories: 1425 ;Fat: 96 g; Protein: 140 g; Carbs: 26 g

DAY 4:

- Breakfast: Carnivore Egg Cups
- Lunch: Oven-Roasted Beef Brisket
- Snack: Beef Jerky
- Dinner: Grilled Wild Duck Breast

Total for the day:
Calories: 1425 ;Fat: 96 g; Protein: 140 g; Carbs: 26 g

DAY 5:

- Breakfast: Bacon and Feta Omelet
- Lunch: Oven-Roasted Beef Brisket
- Snack: Camembert & Chili Bacon Balls
- Dinner: Grilled Wild Duck Breast

Total for the day:
Calories: 1921; Fat: 144.5 g; Protein: 127.4 g;
    Carbs: 31.6 g

DAY 6:

- Breakfast: Bacon and Feta Omelet
- Lunch: Bacon-Wrapped Scallops
- Snack: Camembert & Chili Bacon Balls
- Dinner: Grilled Wild Duck Breast

Total for the day:
Calories: 1979;Fat: 161.5 g;Protein: 103.4 g; Carbs:

32.6 g

DAY 7:

- Breakfast: Bacon and Feta Omelet
- Lunch: Bacon-Wrapped Scallops
- Snack: Camembert & Chili Bacon Balls
- Dinner: Grilled Wild Duck Breast

Total for the day:
Calories: 1979;Fat: 161.5 g;Protein: 103.4 g; Carbs:
    32.6 g

Chapter 3

Culinary Basics

Scotch Eggs

Prep time: 15 minutes | Cook time: 40 minutes | Serves 4

- 4 eggs
- 1 pound pork sausage (ground pork)
- 2 cups pork rinds

1. Cook your eggs to desired doneness.
2. Peel cooked eggs and chill, uncovered, for at least an hour in the refrigerator. This helps the exterior to dry out so the sausage will stick without needing a starch to bind.
3. As the eggs chill, crush pork rinds by placing in a heavy duty zip-top bag and crushing well with a rolling pin or pulse in a food processor until fine crumbs are made.
4. Serve immediately or keep at room temperature for 2-3 hours before serving (as in packing for lunch).

PER SERVING

Calories: 542| Fat: 45g | Protein: 31g | Carbs:2 g

Smoked Sea Salt

Prep time: 5 minutes| Cook time: 8 to 12 hours | Serves 1½

- 1 pound fine sea salt
- Spray bottle of water, smoker, wood chips (optional)

1. If using wood chips, cover them with water and allow to soak for 30 minutes.
2. Start the smoker, following the manufacturer's instructions. If the smoker came with a water bowl, add water to it.
3. Spread the salt on a rimmed baking sheet and spray it lightly with water. Place the baking sheet in the smoker and secure the lid so that it is airtight and no smoke can escape.
4. Once finished, remove the salt from the smoker and allow to cool completely. Store in airtight containers in the pantry for up to a month.

PER SERVING

Calories: 0 | Fat: 0 g | Protein: 0 g | Carbs: 0 g

Salted Beef Stock

Prep time: 5 minutes | Cook time: about 2 hours | Serves 4

- 2-3 pounds marrow bones or osso bucco + bones reserved from previous meals
- 1 tablespoon sea salt, or to taste

1. Turn your instant pot to saute – and adjust to medium. Allow pot to preheat for a minute or two, and then add your marrow bones. Fill to the 'max' line on the stainless steel pot with filtered water.
2. Place lid on and adjust valve to 'seal'. Set instant pot to pressure cook, 90 minutes. After cooking, allow pressure to release naturally, this can take up to 30 minutes.
3. Pour stock into jars using a funnel. Store stock in the refrigerator for up to 3 weeks.

PER SERVING

Calories: 100| Fat: 6 g | Protein: 10 g | Carbs: 0 g

Tahini Sauce

Prep time: 10 minutes | Cook time: 20 minutes | Makes 1½ cups

- ½ cup tahini
- ½ cup warm water
- 2 tablespoons fresh lemon juice
- ½ teaspoon salt
- ¼ teaspoon ground cumin
- 2 tablespoons extra-virgin olive oil

1. In a blender, combine the tahini, water, lemon juice, garlic, monk fruit sweetener (if using), salt, and cumin and blend on medium speed for 30 seconds, or until the ingredients are incorporated.
2. with the blender running, slowly add the oil, mixing until the tahini is fully incorporated and increases slightly in volume. Store in the refrigerator in an airtight container for up to 6 months.

PER SERVING

Calories: 82 | Fat: 8g | Carbs: 3g | Fiber: 1g

Chicken Stock

Prep time: 15 minutes | Cook time: 45 minutes |
Serves 4

- 2 pounds chicken drumsticks or wings
- 3 cloves garlic, peeled
- 1 tablespoon sea salt

1. Place all ingredients in the Instant Pot stainless steel pot with filtered water.
2. Place lid on and adjust valve to 'seal'. After cooking, allow pressure to release naturally, this can take up to 30 minutes.
3. Pour stock into jars using a funnel. Store stock in the refrigerator for up to 3 weeks.

PER SERVING

Calories: 1401| Fat:23g | Protein: 146g | Carbs: 23g

Scrambled Eggs and Cream

Prep time: 15 minutes | Cook time: 15 minutes |
Serves 3

- 1 tablespoon butter
- 3 eggs
- 2 tablespoons heavy cream
- 1/4 teaspoon sea salt

1. In a medium skillet, melt butter over medium heat. As skillet heats, use a fork or whisk to whisk eggs and cream.
2. Scramble eggs until just before set, then remove from heat and sprinkle with sea salt. Enjoy!

PER SERVING

Calories: 333| Fat: 26g | Protein: 19g | Carbs:2 g

Seafood Stock

Prep time: 15 minutes | Cook time: 45 minutes | Serves 4

- 2 pounds seafood shells and/or heads (such as shrimp, lobster, crab)
- 4 cups water
- Salt to taste

1. Rinse the seafood shells and heads under cold water to remove any debris. If using whole shrimp. Use only the shells and heads for the stock.
2. Once cooled, you can store the seafood stock in an airtight container in the refrigerator for up to 3 days, or freeze it for longer storage.

PER SERVING

Calories: 20| Fat: 1g | Protein: 1g | Carbs:2 g

Italian Vinaigrette

Prep time: 5 minutes | Cook time: 20 minutes | Makes ¾ cup

- ½ cup extra-virgin olive oil
- ¼ cup fresh lemon juice
- 2 teaspoons salt
- 1 teaspoon dried basil
- ½ teaspoon dried oregano
- ¼ teaspoon ground cumin

1. In a small screw-top jar, combine the olive oil, lemon juice, salt, basil, oregano, and cumin.
2. Close and shake well to combine. Store unused vinaigrette in the refrigerator for up to 1 week.

PER SERVING

Calories: 162 | Fat: 18g | Carbs: 1g | Fiber: 0g

Salt-Cured Egg Yolks

Prep time: 10 minutes | Cook time: none | Serves 6

- 1 cup fine sea salt or smoked sea salt, store-bought or homemade
- 6 large egg yolks
- Special Equipment:
- Cheesecloth

1. Place the salt in a small shallow casserole dish. The salt should be about ½ inch deep; add more if needed. Use a spoon to make a rounded indentation for each of the yolks. Use your hands to gently cover all the yolks with the salt.
2. Place the dish in the refrigerator for 1 week or until the yolks are dried. Store in the hanging cheesecloth in the fridge for up to a year.

PER SERVING

Calories: 55 | Fat: 5 g | Protein: 3 g | Carbs: 1 g

Teriyaki Sauce

Prep time: 10 minutes | Cook time: 35 minutes |Makes ½ cup

- 1 teaspoon unflavored gelatin (optional)
- 1 tablespoon cold water (optional)
- 1 tablespoon butter
- ½ teaspoon minced fresh ginger
- ½ teaspoon salt

1. If using, sprinkle the gelatin over the cold water in small bowl; let sit for 3 minutes.
2. In a small saucepan, combine the coconut aminos, vinegar, honey, butter, ginger, and salt and cook over low heat until the butter melts. Whisk in the gelatin mixture (if using). Cool completely.
3. Store any leftovers tightly covered in the refrigerator for up to 1 week. If using gelatin, the sauce is best used fresh.

PER SERVING

Calories: 37 | Fat: 1g | Carbs: 7g | Protein: 0g

Chicken Bone Broth

Prep time: 15 minutes | Cook time: 24 hours | Makes 4 quarts

- 1 whole chicken (3 to 4 pounds)
- 8 to 10 chicken feet
- 2 to 3 chicken heads (optional)
- 16 cups water
- 1 tablespoon chopped fresh parsley
- 1 teaspoon salt, plus more to taste

1. Place the chicken in a 6-quart slow cooker and add the chicken feet, chicken heads (if using), celeriac, carrots, and bay leaves. Pour the water over all. Cover and cook on low for 24 hours, adding the parsley and salt the last 30 minutes of cooking.
2. Strain the broth through a fine-mesh strainer; discard the solids. Fasten the lids and store in the refrigerator for up to 7 days or in the freezer for up to 1 year.

PER SERVING

Calories: 45 | Fat: 1.5g | Carbs: 1g | Protein: 7g

Homemade Butter

Prep time: 15 minutes | Cook time: 10 minutes |Makes 1 pound butter, plus 2 cups buttermilk

- 1 quart heavy cream or cultured cream
- Salt to taste

1. Place the cream in the large mixing bowl of a stand mixer with a whisk attachment. Beat on medium-high until the cream starts to separate from the buttermilk, 2 to 3 minutes. You will have a ball of yellow butter in a pool of white buttermilk.
2. Store the butter and buttermilk in separate tightly covered containers in the refrigerator. The butter will keep for up to 3 weeks in the fridge, and the buttermilk will keep for 2 weeks in the fridge.

PER SERVING

Calories: 108 | Fat: 12g | Carbs: 0g | Protein: 0g

Chapter 4

Breakfast Bonanza

Carnivore Egg Cups

Prep time: 5 minutes | Cook time: 12 minutes |
  Serves 6

- Lard or tallow, for the pan
- 6 slices deli roast beef
- 6 tablespoons Easy Carnivore Hollandaise, for serving (optional)

1. Preheat the oven to 400°F. Grease a 6-well muffin pan.
2. Place 1 slice of roast beef into each well. Place a slice of cheese into each beef-lined cup. Then break an egg into each beef cup.
3. Serve with hollandaise, if desired.
4. Store in an airtight container in the refrigerator for up to 4 days preheated 350°F oven for 5 minutes, or until heated through.

PER SERVING

Calories: 641 | Fat: 52 g | Protein: 38 g | Carbs: 1 g

Bacon and Feta Omelet

Prep time: 5 minutes | Cook time: 25 minutes |
  Serves 4

- 8 bacon slices
- 4 tablespoons salted butter
- 4 eggs, beaten
- 1 cup feta cheese, crumbled

1. Preheat the oven to 400°F. Line a baking sheet with parchment paper and place the bacon on it. Cook for 15 minutes (or to desired crispiness), flipping at the halfway point. Remove from the oven and crumble. Set aside.
2. In a medium sauté pan, melt the butter over medium heat.
3. Serve hot or store in an airtight container in the refrigerator for up to 3 days.

PER SERVING

Calories: 804 | Fat: 66g | Carbs: 4g | Protein: 46g

Ham Hocks and Fried Eggs

Prep time: 5 minutes | Cook time: 10 minutes | Serves 4

- 4 (10-ounce) smoked ham hocks
- 1 tablespoon lard or tallow
- 4 large eggs
- ¼ teaspoon fine sea salt

1. Preheat the oven to 425°F.
2. Place the ham hocks on a rimmed baking sheet. Bake for 10 minutes, or until the skin gets crispy.
3. Meanwhile, fry the eggs: Heat the lard in a large cast-iron skillet over low heat. Remove the eggs from the pan.
4. Place a ham hock along with a fried egg on a plate. Top with 2 tablespoons of hollandaise, if using. Best served immediately.

PER SERVING

Calories: 462 | Fat: 37 g | Protein: 30 g | Carbs: 0.4 g

Tuna Salad Deviled Eggs

Prep time: 5 minutes | Cook time: 15 minutes |Serves 4

- 4 eggs
- 1 (6-ounce) can tuna, drained
- 1/2 red onions, chopped
- 1 serrano pepper, minced
- 1/4 teaspoon cayenne pepper
- 1/4 teaspoon basil

1. Arrange the eggs in a small saucepan. Heat off and let it sit, covered, for 9 to 10 minutes.
2. When the eggs are cool enough to handle, separate the egg whites and yolks.
3. Mash the yolks with the remaining ingredients until everything is well incorporated. Divide the yolk mixture among egg whites. Enjoy!

PER SERVING

Calories: 112 | Fat: 4.7g | Carbs: 2.3g | Protein: 14.5g

Bacon, Egg, and Cheese Cups

Prep time: 10 minutes | Cook time: 30 minutes | Serves 4

- 8 bacon slices
- 3 tablespoons salted butter
- 10 eggs
- 2 teaspoons sea salt
- ½ cup shredded cheddar cheese

1. Preheat the oven to 375°F. Cook for 15 minutes, flipping at the halfway point.
2. Meanwhile, grease a 12-cup muffin tin thoroughly with the butter.
3. Serve hot or store in an airtight container in the refrigerator for up to 3 days.

PER SERVING

Calories: 420 | Fat: 33g | Carbs: 1g | Protein: 27g

Scrambled Eggs in a Mug

Prep time: 5 minutes | Cook time: 5 minutes | Serves 2

- 4 eggs
- 2 tablespoons milk
- Flaky salt, to taste
- 1/4 teaspoon ground black pepper

1. Beat the eggs in a microwave-safe mug; add in the milk and beat until frothy and light yellow.
2. Heat the eggs in your microwave until cooked through approximately 1 ½ minutes.
3. Sprinkle salt and black pepper over the eggs. Enjoy!

PER SERVING

Calories: 142 | Fat: 9.4g | Carbs: 2.5g | Protein: 12.1g

Sausage Cakes with Poached Eggs

Prep time: 20 minutes | Cook time: 11 minutes |Serves 4

- 1 pound sausage patties
- 2 tbsp olive oil
- 1 tbsp cilantro, chopped

1. Fry the sausage patties in warm oil 2 cups of water in a pot over high heat, and reduce to simmer, without boiling.
2. Crack each egg into a small bowl and gently put the egg into the simmering cilantro, salt, and black pepper to serve.

PER SERVING

Calories: 523 | Fat: 43g | Carbs: 2.5g | Protein 28g

Chorizo Sausage Egg Cakes

Prep time: 15 minutes | Cook time: 10 minutes |Serves 4

- 2 tsp butter, melted
- 8 eggs, beaten
- Salt and black pepper to taste
- 2 cups mozzarella cheese, grated
- 4 chorizo, cooked and chopped

1. In a bowl, stir the eggs, sausages and cheese; season with salt and pepper.
2. Add into greased with butter muffin cups, and bake in the oven for 8-10 minutes at 400°F.

PER SERVING

Calories: 512 | Fat 35.5g | Carbs: 5.4g | Protein 41g

Classic Eggs with Canadian Bacon

Prep time: 5 minutes | Cook time: 15 minutes |Serves 3

- 3 (1-ounce) slices Canadian bacon
- 6 eggs
- ½ teaspoon ground black pepper
- Salt, to season

1. Heat up a nonstick aluminum pan over a medium-high flame. Once hot, fry the bacon until crispy; reserve, living the rendered fat in the pan.
2. Turn the heat to medium-low. Crack the eggs into the bacon grease. Cover the pan with a lid and fry the eggs until they are cooked through.
3. Salt and pepper to taste. Enjoy!

PER SERVING

Calories: 326 | Fat: 13.3g | Carbs: 5.2g | Protein: 16g

Ham Cheese Egg Cups

Prep time: 5 minutes | Cook time: 15 minutes |Serves 9

- 9 slices ham
- Coarse salt and ground black pepper, to season
- 1/2 cup Swiss cheese, shredded
- 9 eggs

1. Begin by preheating your oven to 390 degrees F. Lightly grease a muffin pan with cooking spray.
2. Line each cup with a slice of ham; add salt, black pepper, jalapeno, and cheese. Crack an egg into each ham cup.
3. Bake in the preheated oven about 13 minutes or until the eggs are cooked through. Bon appétit!

PER SERVING

Calories: 137| Fat: 8.6g | Carbs: 1.8g | Protein: 12g

Chapter 5

Snack Attack and Appetizers

Smoked Salmon Deviled Eggs

Prep time: 10 minutes | Cook time: none | Serves 4

- 6 large hard-boiled eggs
- 2 ounces low-fat cream cheese
- 2 tablespoons mayonnaise
- ½ teaspoon dried dill
- ¼ teaspoon mustard powder
- Smoked paprika, for garnish (optional)
- Fresh dill, for garnish (optional)

1. Halve each egg lengthwise. Remove the yolks and add to a mixing bowl with the cream cheese, mayonnaise, dill, mustard powder, salt, and pepper. Use a fork to mash into a smooth mixture, combining until creamy with no chunks remaining.
2. Flake the smoked salmon apart and layer on top. Garnish with smoked paprika or fresh dill, if desired, and serve.

PER SERVING

Calories: 160 | Fat: 11g | Carbos: 3g | Protein: 11g

Beef Jerky

Prep time: 15 minutes | Cook time: 5 hours | Serves 5

- 1 pound (97-percent lean) ground beef
- 1 teaspoon onion powder
- 1 teaspoon freshly ground black pepper
- 1 teaspoon garlic powder
- ¼ teaspoon curing salt

1. Preheat the oven to 200°F. Line a baking sheet with aluminum foil.
2. Onto the prepared baking sheet, pipe the meat mixture into 4-inch strips, making rows until you use all of the meat.
3. Bake for 3 to 5 hours, or until the jerky bends but doesn't break. (Check the jerky after 3 hours. If it breaks, it's not done cooking yet.)
4. Cool for 2 hours before storing in an airtight container for up to 1 week.

PER SERVING

Calories: 123 | Fat: 5g | Carbos: 1g | Protein: 20g

Pig Candy

**Prep time:10 minutes | Cook time: 20 minutes |
Serves 4**

- ½ cup dark brown sugar
- ⅛ tsp. cayenne pepper
- 1 lb. thick cut bacon strips
- ¼ cup maple syrup

1. Mix cayenne pepper and brown sugar in a small bowl.
2. Drizzle this mixture over the bacon strips.
3. Brush the bacon with maple syrup and cook for 10 minutes more.
4. Serve.

PER SERVING:

Calories: 85 | Fat: 8g | Carbs: 25g | Protein: 1g

Ranch and Blue Cheese Dip

**Prep time: 5 minutes | Cook time: 10 minutes
|Serves 10**

- 1/2 cup Greek-style yogurt
- 1 cup blue cheese, crumbled
- 1/2 cup mayonnaise
- 1 tablespoon lime juice
- Freshly ground black pepper, to taste
- 2 tablespoons ranch seasoning

1. In a mixing bowl, thoroughly combine all ingredients until well incorporated.
2. Serve well chilled with your favorite keto dippers. Bon appétit!

PER SERVING

Calories: 94 | Fat: 8.1g | Carbs: 1.3g | Fiber: 0.1g

Crispy Chicken Nuggets

Prep time: 25 minutes | Cook time: 20 minutes |Serves 4

- 2 tbsp ranch dressing
- ½ cup almond flour
- 1 egg
- 2 tbsp garlic powder
- 4 chicken breasts, cubed
- Salt and black pepper, to taste
- 1 tbsp butter, melted

1. Preheat oven to 400 F and grease a baking dish with the butter.
2. In a bowl, combine salt, garlic powder, flour, and pepper, and stir. In a separate bowl, beat egg. Add the chicken to the egg mixture, then in the flour mixture. Bake for 18-20 minutes, turning halfway through. Remove to paper towels, drain the excess grease and serve with ranch dressing.

PER SERVING

Calories: 473 | Fat: 31g | Carbs: 7.6g | Protein 43g

Cheesy Chicken Dip

Prep time: 10 minutes|Cook time: 25 minutes|- Serves 8

- 2 chicken breasts, cooked and shredded
- ½ cup hot sauce
- 8 ounces of cream cheese, softened
- 1 cup Mozzarella cheese, shredded
- ¼ cup Blue cheese, crumbled
- ½ cup ranch dressing
- 1 cup Cheddar cheese, shredded

1. Place the cooking pot in the Ninja Foodi Grill main unit.
2. In a mixing bowl, add all and mix well.
3. Pour bowl mixture into the greased baking dish.
4. Press Bake mode, set the temperature to 350°F, and set time to 25 minutes. Press Start.
5. Cover with lid and cook for 25 minutes.

PER SERVING

Calories: 256 | Fat: 19.2g | Carbs: 2.2g | Fiber: 0.1g

Pesto Cheese Dip

Prep time: 10 minutes | Cook time: 12 minutes | Serves 8

- ⅓ cup basil pesto
- 1 cup Mozzarella cheese, shredded
- 8 ounces of cream cheese, softened
- ¼ cup Parmesan cheese, grated
- ½ cup roasted peppers

1. Place the cooking pot in the Ninja Foodi Smart XL Grill.
2. Add all ingredients into the bowl and mix until well-combined.
3. Pour mixture into the greased baking dish.
4. Select the Bake Mode and set the temperature to 350 degrees F.
5. Cover the hood and allow the grill to cook.
6. Serve, when done.

PER SERVING:

Calories: 112 | Fat: 10.6g | Carbs 1.6g | Fiber: 0.2g

Camembert & Chili Bacon Balls

Prep time: 15 minutes | Cook time: 5 minutes |Serves 4

- 1 cup bacon, finely chopped
- 5 oz camembert cheese, cubed
- 1 chili pepper, seeded and chopped
- ¼ tsp parsley flakes
- ½ tsp paprika

1. Fry the bacon in a pan over medium heat until crispy; about 5 minutes. Let cool for a few minutes.
2. Place the camembert cheese, chili pepper, parsley, and paprika in a bowl and mix to combine well. Create balls from the mixture. Set the cooled bacon in a plate. Roll the balls around to coat all sides.

PER SERVING

Calories: 456 | Fat 39.5g | Carbs: 3.6g | Protein 22.4g

Carnivore Frosting

Prep time: 5 minutes | Cook time: 1 hour 30 minutes | Serves 4

- 1 beef femur bone, canoe cut (2 canoe-cut bones)
- 1 tablespoon honey
- ⅛ teaspoon salt

1. Preheat the oven to 400°F. Line a roasting pan with foil or parchment paper.
2. Place the bones, marrow-side up, in the roasting pan. Roast until the marrow is soft, 20 to 30 minutes. Let cool.
3. Store any leftovers tightly covered in the refrigerator for up to 5 days, or in the freezer for up to 6 months. If frozen, allow to thaw in the refrigerator overnight before use.

PER SERVING

Calories: 197 | Fat: 21g | Carbs: 4g | Protein: 2g

Creamy Chicken Dip

Prep time: 10 minutes | Cook time: 25 minutes | Serves 6

- 2 cups chicken, cooked and shredded
- 4 tablespoons hot sauce
- ¼ teaspoon garlic powder
- ½ cup sour cream
- 8 ounces of cream cheese, softened

1. Place the cooking pot in the Ninja Foodi Smart XL Grill.
2. Add all ingredients to a bowl and mix until well combined.
3. Transfer mixture in a greased baking dish.
4. Select the Bake Mode and set the temperature to 350 degrees F.
5. Cover the hood and allow the grill to cook.
6. Serve, when done.

PER SERVING

Calories: 245 | Fat: 18.7g | Carbs: 2.1g | Fiber: 0g

Chapter 6

Salads, Sides, and More

Corned Lamb Hearts

Prep time: 15 minutes | Cook time: 72 hours | Serves 4

- 3 cups water, plus more if needed
- 2 tablespoons honey
- 2 tablespoons salt
- ⅛ teaspoon ground Ceylon cinnamon
- ⅛ teaspoon dried thyme
- 4 lamb hearts (1 pound total)

1. In a small saucepan, combine 2 cups of the water, the honey, salt, cinnamon, thyme, rosemary, and bay leaves. Bring to a boil; reduce the heat. Simmer, uncovered, for 5 minutes. Cool completely.
2. Let the hearts cool in brine. Reserve the brine to store any leftover heart.
3. Store the heart and some of the brine in a tightly covered container in the refrigerator for up to 5 days.

PER SERVING

Calories: 180 | Fat: 8g | Carbs: 2g | Protein: 25g

Chicken Wings

Prep time: 7 minutes | Cook time: 32 minutes | Serves 4

- 1 pound chicken wings or drummies
- 1 teaspoon fine sea salt

1. Preheat the oven or an air fryer to 350°F. If using the oven, line a rimmed baking sheet with parchment paper.
2. Season the chicken wings on all sides with the salt. Place the wings on the lined baking sheet or in the air fryer basket in a single layer.
3. Cook for 25 minutes, flipping the wings over after 15 minutes.
4. After 25 minutes, increase the oven or air fryer temperature to 400°F and cook for 6 to 7 more minutes, or until the skin is browned and crisp.

PER SERVING

Calories: 325 | Fat: 22 g | Protein: 30 g | Carbs: 0 g

Classic Hot Chicken Drumettes

Prep time: 5 minutes | Cook time: 25 minutes |Serves 6

- 2 pounds chicken drumettes
- 1 teaspoon cayenne pepper
- 1 teaspoon dried oregano
- 1 tablespoon stone-ground mustard
- 1 teaspoon garlic powder

1. Pat dry the chicken drumettes with paper towels cayenne pepper, and oregano.
2. Brush the drumettes with cooking oil and transfer to a roasting pan. Bake at 420 degrees F for 18 minutes.
3. Toss with the hot sauce, mustard and garlic powder; broil for 5 minutes more golden brown and thoroughly cooked. Bon appétit!

PER SERVING

Calories: 179 | Fat: 2.5g | Carbs: 2.3g | Protein: 34.2g

The Real Meat-Lover's Pizza

Prep time: 15 minutes | Cook time: 1 hour 20 minutes | Serves 8

For The Crust
- 6 ounces cooked chicken, chopped
- 3 ounces pork rinds
- 2 ounces Parmesan cheese, shredded
- 1 large egg yolk
- 3 to 4 fresh basil leaves

1. In a blender or food processor, combine the chicken, pork rinds, Transfer to a medium bowl and chill until firm, about 30 minutes.
2. Preheat the oven to 400°F.
3. Divide the dough into two portions and shape each into a ball.
4. Spread the nomato sauce over the pizza crust and top with the mozzarella and basil.

PER SERVING

Calories: 356 | Fat: 16g | Carbs: 9g | Protein: 44g

Beef Heart Recipe

Prep time: 15 minutes | Cook time:1 hour 15 minutes | Serves 4

- 1 beef heart (approx 3-4 lbs) or 8 ounces as called for in this meal plan this week.
- 1 teaspoon sea salt
- 2 cups filtered water

1. If not cut in half, cut beef heart in half and remove any hard bits (it may already be trimmed and there is nothing to do). Pour water around the salted beef heart.
2. Place the lid on the Instant Pot, and set to 'seal'. Cook on high pressure for 75 minutes on high pressure. Allow pressure to release naturally for at least 15 minutes.
3. Slice thinly against the grain, salt as desired, and enjoy warm or cool.

PER SERVING

Calories: 1554| Fat: 111g | Protein: 122g | Carbs:9 g

Chipotle Shrimp Cakes

Prep time: 15 minutes | Cook time: 12 minutes | Serves 4

- 1 pound shrimp, peeled, deveined, and roughly chopped
- ¼ cup chopped shallot
- 1 teaspoon grated lemon zest
- ¼ cup coconut flour
- 2 tablespoons extra-virgin olive oil, divided

1. In a large bowl, stir together the shrimp, shallot, lemon zest, oregano, garlic powder, and chipotle powder.
2. Add the eggs and stir to coat. Stir in the coconut flour. Set aside for 5 minutes, until the mixture thickens.
3. In a large nonstick skillet, heat 1 tablespoon of olive oil over medium heat until hot. Repeat with the remaining shrimp cakes and 1 tablespoon of olive oil.

PER SERVING

Calories: 239 | Fat: 11g | Carbs: 6g | Fiber: 1g

Creamed Monkfish Salad

Prep time: 5 minutes | Cook time: 20 minutes |Serves 5

- 2 pounds monkfish
- 1 tablespoon balsamic vinegar
- 1/2 cup mayonnaise
- 1 teaspoon stone-ground mustard
- Flaky salt, to season

1. Pat the fish dry with paper towels flipping halfway through for about 9 minutes or until opaque.
2. Flake the fish with a fork and toss with the remaining ingredients; gently toss to combine well.
3. Serve at room temperature or well-chilled. Bon appétit!

PER SERVING

Calories: 306 | Fat: 19.4g | Carbs: 3.8g | Protein: 27g

Ranch Bacon Chips

Prep time: 5 minutes | Cook time:15 minutes |Serves 12

- 1 ½ pounds bacon, cut into 1-inch squares
- 1/4 cup lemon juice
- 1 teaspoon Ranch seasoning mix
- 1 tablespoon hot sauce

1. Toss the bacon squares with the lemon juice, Ranch seasoning mix, and hot sauce. Arrange the bacon squares on a parchment-lined baking sheet.
2. Roast in the preheated oven at 375 degrees F approximately 10 minutes or until crisp.
3. Let it cool completely before storing. Bon appétit!

PER SERVING

Calories: 232 | Fat: 22.4g | Carbs: 0.8g | Protein: 7.1g | Fiber: 0g

Chicken Liver Pate

Prep time: 15 minutes | Cook time: 15 minutes | Serves 4

- 1 pound chicken livers, soaked
- Filtered water
- 1/4 cup tallow
- 1 two-ounce can of anchovies, drained

1. Over medium heat in a large saucepan, Pour all the melted tallow and cooked liver in a food processor.
2. Process until well pureed and all of the ingredients are well combined.
3. Scoop into ramekins and then top with melted tallow if desired. Store covered in the freezer for up to 6 months or in the refrigerator for up to 10 days.

PER SERVING

Calories: 60| Fat: 4g | Protein: 4g | Carbs:0 g

Sautéed Beef Kidney

Prep time: 10 minutes | Cook time: 15 minutes | Serves 4

- 4 tablespoons salted butter
- 4 beef kidneys, sliced thin

1. In a large sauté pan, melt the butter over medium-high heat. Add the kidney slices. Cook for about 5 minutes, flipping the slices halfway through, until barely any pink remains.
2. Remove from the heat and let rest for 5 minutes. Be careful not to overcook.
3. Serve immediately or store in an airtight container in the refrigerator for up to 2 days.

PER SERVING

Calories: 428 | Fat: 30g | Carbs: 1g | Protein: 40g

Chapter 7

Beef and Lamb Extravaganza

Baked Lamb and Feta Patties

Prep time: 5 minutes | Cook time: 12 minutes | Serves 6

- 1½ pounds ground lamb
- 4 ounces feta cheese, crumbled
- 2 teaspoons smoked sea salt, store-bought or homemade, or fine sea salt

1. Preheat the oven to 350°F.
2. Place the ingredients in a large bowl and use your hands to thoroughly them on a rimmed baking sheet.
3. Bake for 10 to 12 minutes, until the patties are cooked through.
4. Store in an airtight container in the preheated 350°F oven for 5 minutes, or until heated through.

PER SERVING

Calories: 327 | Fat: 25 g | Protein: 22 g | Carbs: 1 g

Grilled Lamb Kofta

Prep time: 5 minutes | Cook time: 8 minutes | Serves 4

- 1 pound ground lamb or ground beef
- 1¾ teaspoons fine sea salt
- Melted tallow or lard, for greasing
- 12 (8-inch) metal or wooden skewers

1. If using wooden skewers, soak them in water for 10 minutes. Preheat a grill to medium heat.
2. Serve with goat cheese on the side, if desired.
3. Store in an airtight container in the refrigerator for up to 4 days. To reheat, place in a lightly greased skillet over medium heat for 4 minutes or until heated through.

PER SERVING

Calories: 283 | Fat: 22 g | Protein: 19 g | Carbs: 0 g

Grilled Beef Short Loin

Prep time: 5 minutes | Cook time:30 minutes | Serves 3

- 1 ½ pounds beef short loin
- 2 thyme sprigs, chopped
- 1 rosemary sprig, chopped
- 1 teaspoon garlic powder
- Sea salt and ground black pepper, to taste

1. Place all of the above ingredients in a re-sealable zipper bag. Shake until the beef short loin is well coated on all sides.
2. Cook on a preheated grill for 15 to 20 minutes, flipping once or twice during the cooking time.
3. Let it stand for 5 minutes before slicing and serving. Bon appétit!

PER SERVING

Calories: 313| Fat: 11.6g | Carbs: 0.1g | Protein: 52g | Fiber: 0.1g

Oven-Roasted Beef Brisket

Prep time: 35 minutes | Cook time: 6 hours | Serves 5

- 2 tablespoons kosher salt
- 1 teaspoon freshly ground black pepper
- 1½ teaspoons garlic powder
- 1 teaspoon onion powder
- 1 (3-pound) brisket

1. Preheat the oven to 300°F. Line a baking sheet with aluminum foil.
2. Roast for about 4 hours or until the thickest part of the brisket reaches 200°F.
3. Transfer the brisket to a cutting board to rest for 30 minutes. Slice across the grain.
4. Serve immediately or store in an airtight container in the refrigerator for up to 3 days.

PER SERVING

Calories: 364 | Fat: 14g | Carbs: 1g | Protein: 59g

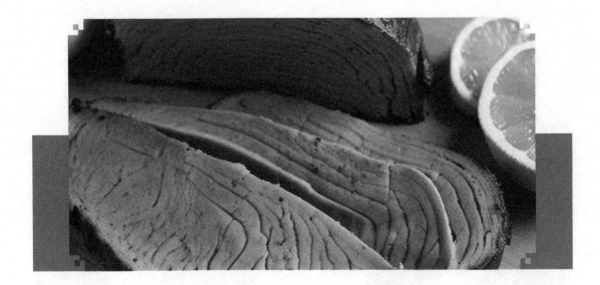

Swedish Roast Beef

Prep time: 15 minutes | Cook time: 16 hours |
Serves 8

- 1 boneless beef rump roast or other lean beef roast (3 to 4 pounds), frozen
- For The Brine
- 2 cups water, room temperature
- ½ cup salt
- 2 cups ice water
- 3 tablespoons honey

1. Preheat the oven to 200°F. Place the frozen roast on a rack in a shallow roasting pan.
2. Remove the roast from the brine and pat dry with paper towels. Slice the meat against the grain and serve.
3. Store the meat tightly covered in the refrigerator for up to 5 days.

PER SERVING

Calories: 346 | Fat: 14g | Carbs: 6g | Protein: 49g

Zesty Grilled Ham

Prep time: 15 minutes|Cook time: 10 minutes|-
Serves 4

- ⅓ cup packed brown sugar
- 2 tbsp. prepared horseradish
- 4 tsp. lemon juice
- 1 (1 lb.) fully cooked bone-in ham steak

1. Boil brown sugar, lemon juice and horseradish in a small saucepan.
2. Soak the ham slices in this mixture and coat well.
3. Select the "Grill" Mode, set the temperature to MED.
4. Press the START/STOP button to initiate preheating.
5. Once preheated, place the ham in the Ninja Foodi grill.
6. Cover the hood and allow the grill to cook.
7. Serve warm.

PER SERVING

Calories 180 | Fat 5g | Carbs 20g | Protein 14g

BBQ Beef Short Ribs

Prep time: 5 minutes|Cook time: 50 minutes|-Serves2

- 2 Beef Short Ribs
- ¼ cup Red Wine
- ¾ cup Beef Stock
- Onion Powder
- 1 tbsp cornstarch

1. Season the beef ribs with the seasonings.
2. Add the wine, and broth to the bottom of the Foodi cooking bowl.
3. Close the toggle switch to sealing.
4. Remove the ribs to rest and take out the rack.
5. Mix up the slurry and pour into the pan juices in the pot to thicken.
6. Spoon over the ribs and enjoy!

PER SERVING

Calories 906 | Carbohydrates 78g | Protein 50g | Fat 22g | Sodium 2667mg| Fiber 3g

Awesome Beef Cheeseburgers

Prep time: 20 minutes | Cook time: 5 minutes |Serves 4

- 1 pound ground beef
- 1 spring onion, chopped
- Salt, black and cayenne pepper
- 1 tsp yellow mustard
- 1 oz cheddar cheese, grated
- 1 tbsp olive oil

1. To a mixing bowl, add ground beef, cayenne pepper, black pepper, spring onion, and salt. Shape into 2 balls; then flatten to make burgers.
2. In a separate bowl, mix mustard with cheddar cheese. Split the cheese mixture between the prepared patties. Cook the burgers for 5 minutes on each side.

PER SERVING

Calories: 386 | Fat 25.5g | Carbs: 1.3g | Protein 31.6g

Stuffed Lamb Shoulder

Prep time: 1 hour | Cook time: 45 minutes| Serves 4

- 1 lb rolled lamb shoulder, boneless
- 1 ½ cups basil leaves, chopped
- 5 tbsp macadamia nuts, chopped
- ½ cup green olives, chopped
- 2 garlic cloves, minced
- Salt and black pepper to taste

1. In a bowl, combine basil, macadamia, olives, and garlic. Season lamb with salt and pepper.
2. Spread with the previously prepared mixture, roll up the lamb and tie it together using 3 strings of butcher's twine. Place lamb onto a greased baking dish and cook in the oven for 45 minutes at 380 F. When ready, transfer the meat to a chopping board, and let it rest for 10 minutes before slicing.

PER SERVING
Calories: 5573| Fat: 41g | Carbs: 3.1g | Protein: 37g

Beef Heart and Liver Meatballs

Prep time: 10 minutes | Cook time: 25 minutes | Serves 4

- 8 ounces ground beef
- 4 ounces ground beef heart
- 4 ounces ground liver
- 1 teaspoon sea salt

1. Preheat the oven to 350°F. Line a baking sheet with aluminum foil.
2. In a medium bowl, mix the ground beef, beef heart, and liver until well combined. Season with the salt. Roll the mixture into 2-inch balls and place them on the prepared baking sheet.
3. Bake for 25 minutes or until the meatballs are firm and cooked through.
4. Serve immediately or store in an airtight container in the refrigerator for up to 3 days.

PER SERVING
Calories: 140 | Fat: 5g | Carbohydrates: 0g | Protein: 22g

Grilled Mediterranean Lamb Chops

Prep time: 25 minutes | Cook time: 2 hours | Serves 4

- 8 lamb loin chops
- 2 cloves garlic, minced
- 2 tablespoons fresh rosemary, chopped
- 2 tablespoons olive oil
- 1 lemon, juiced
- Salt and black pepper to taste

1. In a small bowl, combine minced garlic, chopped rosemary, thyme, oregano, olive oil, lemon juice, salt, and black pepper. Mix well to create a marinade.
2. Preheat grill to medium-high heat.
3. Remove lamb chops from the marinade and discard any excess marinade.
4. Once cooked, remove lamb chops from the grill and let them rest for a few minutes before serving.

PER SERVING

Calories: 350 | Fat: 22g | Carbs: 2g | Protein: 32g

Smoked Beef Roast

Prep time: 5 minutes | Cook time: 3 hours | Serves 12

- 1 (5-pound) boneless beef roast
- 2½ tablespoons fine sea salt
- Special Equipment:
- Smoker, wood chips (optional)

1. If using wood chips, cover them with water and allow to soak for 30 minutes. Season the roast on all sides with the salt.
2. Remove the roast from the smoker and allow to rest for 10 minutes before slicing.
3. Store in an airtight container in the refrigerator for up to 4 days or in the freezer for up to a month. To reheat, place slices on a rimmed baking sheet in a preheated 350°F oven for 5 minutes, or until heated through.

PER SERVING

Calories: 507 | Fat: 33 g | Protein: 49 g | Carbs: 0 g

Chapter 8

Pork Parade

Sous Vide Pork Chop

Prep time: 5 minutes | Cook time: 47 minutes | Serves 1

- 1 bone-in pork chop, about ¾ inch thick
- ¾ teaspoon fine sea salt
- 1½ teaspoons tallow or bacon fat

1. Fill a large pot with water. Set the sous vide machine to 140°F and place it into the pot of water. Season the pork chop on both sides with the salt. Place the chop in the sous vide bag. Seal the bag, making sure no air pockets remain in the bag.
2. Heat the tallow in a cast-iron skillet over medium-high heat. Once the skillet is hot, remove the pork chop from the bag and place in the hot oil. Remove from the heat, allow to rest for 5 minutes, and serve.

PER SERVING

Calories: 305 | Fat: 23 g | Protein: 22 g | Carbs: 0 g

Curried Pork Skewers

Prep time: 10 minutes | Cook time: 23 minutes | Serves 4

- 2 tbsp. fish sauce
- 2 tbsp. Thai thin soy sauce
- 1 tbsp. sugar
- 1 tsp. kosher salt
- 4 oz. fatback, cut into ½ " pieces

1. Mix coconut milk, turmeric, curry powder, black pepper, salt, sugar, soy sauce and fish sauce in a pan.
2. Cook to a boil then reduce its heat and cook for 15 minutes on a simmer.
3. Cover the hood and allow the grill to cook for 8 minutes, flipping halfway through.
4. Serve warm.

PER SERVING

Calories: 429 | Fat: 17g | Carbs: 15g | Fiber: 0g

Baked Balsamic-Glazed Pork Tenderloin

Prep time: 15 minutes | Cook time: 35 minutes | Serves 2 to 4

- 1 pork tenderloin (12 to 16 ounces)
- ½ teaspoon salt
- 4 tablespoons butter
- 2 tablespoons balsamic vinegar
- 1 teaspoon chopped fresh basil
- 1 teaspoon chopped fresh oregano
- 1 teaspoon fresh thyme leaves

1. Preheat the oven to 400°F. Line a rimmed baking sheet with enough foil to wrap the pork. Pat the pork dry with paper towels and rub with the salt.
2. Store leftovers in an airtight container in the fridge for up to 4 days.

PER SERVING

Calories: 439 | Fat: 27g | Carbs: 2g | Protein: 47g

Hot Pork Meatballs

Prep time: 25 minutes | Cook time: 22 minutes |Serves 2

- 1 pound ground pork
- Salt and black pepper, to taste
- 2 tbsp yellow mustard
- ¼ cup mozzarella cheese, grated
- ¼ cup hot sauce
- 1 egg

1. Preheat oven to 400 F and line a baking tray with parchment paper. In a bowl, combine the pork, pepper, mustard, flour, mozzarella cheese, salt, and egg. Form meatballs and arrange them on the baking tray.
2. Cook for 16 minutes, then pour over the hot sauce and bake for 5 more minutes.

PER SERVING

Calories: 487 | Fat: 35g | Carbs: 4.3g | Protein 31.5g

Chili-Spiced Ribs

Prep time: 15 minutes | Cook time: 50 minutes | Serves 6

Glaze:
- 1 cup of soy sauce
- ⅓ cup lemon juice
- 1 ½ teaspoon fresh ginger root, minced

Ribs:
- 6 pounds pork baby back ribs
- 3 tablespoons packed brown sugar
- 1 teaspoon salt

1. Take the first six in a suitable bowl and mix well.
2. Place the cooking pot in the Ninja Foodi Smart XL Grill then place the grill grate in the pot.
3. Grill for another 5 minutes per side.
4. Serve.

PER SERVING:

Calories 305 | Fat 25g | Sodium 532mg | Carbs 2.3g | Fiber 0.4g | Sugar 2g | Protein 18.3g

Shredded Pork Butt Roast

Prep time: 5 minutes | Cook time: 20 minutes | Serves 6

- Pork butt roast, approx 3 pounds
- 1 cup stock or water
- 1 tablespoon sea salt
- 1 tablespoon tallow

1. In Instant Pot, turn to saute-medium and melt tallow. Once preheated, brown pork roast on all sides, about 5-10 minutes each. Sprinkle with sea salt and then add stock or water to the Instant Pot. Cook on high pressure (manual) for 1 hour 15 minutes and then allow pressure to release naturally (this will take another 45ish minutes).
2. Pour juices (stir the fats back in) over shredded meat and add salt to taste.

PER SERVING

Calories: 773| Fat: 59g | Protein: 58g | Carbs:0 g

Pork Rind Waffles

Prep time: 15 minutes | Cook time: 15 minutes | Makes 8 mini waffles

- 4.5 ounces pork rinds
- ½ teaspoon salt
- 4 large eggs
- ¼ cup heavy cream
- Tallow

1. Preheat a waffle maker per manufacturer's directions.
2. Add the pork rinds to a food processor or blender. Cover and process or blend until finely crushed. Transfer to a medium bowl and stir in the salt and baking powder.
3. Store any leftovers tightly covered in the refrigerator for up to 4 days.

PER SERVING

Calories: 394 | Fat: 26g | Carbs: 5g | Protein: 35g

Bacon Buck Burgers

Prep time: 5 minutes | Cook time: 30 minutes | Serves 4

- 12 bacon slices
- 1 pound ground venison
- 4 slices cheddar cheese

1. Preheat the oven to 400°F. Line a baking sheet with parchment paper and place the bacon on it. Cook for 15 minutes (or to desired crispiness), flipping at the halfway point. Remove from the oven and set aside.
2. Form the venison into 4 patties about ½ inch thick.
3. Serve immediately or store in an airtight container in the refrigerator for up to 3 days.

PER SERVING

Calories: 499 | Fat: 36g | Carbs: 1g | Protein: 40g

Chapter 9

Poultry Picks

Braised Rabbit

Prep time: 5 minutes | Cook time: 55 minutes | Serves 8

- ¼ cup tallow or bacon fat
- 1 tablespoon fine sea salt
- 2 cups Carnivore Bone Broth , beef or chicken version

1. Heat the tallow in a large cast-iron skillet over medium-high heat. Season the rabbit pieces on all sides with the salt. Once the skillet is hot, add the meat and cook for 6 minutes, flipping after 3 minutes.
2. Store in an airtight container in the refrigerator for 4 days. To reheat, place in a casserole dish with ½ cup of chicken broth in a preheated 350°F oven for 5 to 8 minutes, or until heated through.

PER SERVING

Calories: 360 | Fat: 19 g | Protein: 44 g | Carbs: 0 g

Feta & Mozzarella Chicken

Prep time: 45 minutes | Cook time: 35 minutes |Serves 4

- 1 pound chicken breasts
- ½ tsp mixed spice seasoning
- Salt and black pepper to season
- 4 oz feta cheese, crumbled
- ½ cup mozzarella, shredded

1. Rub the chicken with spice mix, salt and pepper. Put in a casserole dish over the chicken. Mix oil with feta and mozzarella cheeses, pepper, and stir in 4 tbsp water.
2. Pour the mixture over the chicken and cover the casserole with aluminium foil. Bake in the oven for 20 minutes at 370 F, remove foil and continue cooking for 15 minutes until a nice golden brown color is formed on top.

PER SERVING

Calories: 343 | Fat: 27g | Carbs: 5.2g | Protein 23g

Grilled Wild Duck Breast

**Prep time: 15 minutes | Cook time: 10 minutes |
Serves 8**

- ¼ cup Worcestershire sauce
- 2 tbsp. olive oil
- ½ tsp. hot sauce
- 2 tbsp. garlic, minced
- ¼ tsp. black pepper
- 8 boned duck breast halves

1. Place duck breasts in a tray.
2. Mix oil and rest of the ingredients together and then pour over the duck.
3. Plug the thermometer into the appliance.
4. Cover the hood and allow the grill to cook.
5. Serve warm.

PER SERVING

Calories: 297 | Fat: 25g | Carbs: 23g | Fiber: 0.4g

Roasted Chicken with Creamy Topping

**Prep time: 50 minutes | Cook time: 40 minutes
|Serves 4**

- 1 pound chicken legs
- ¼ cup mascarpone cheese
- 4 tbsp sour cream
- 1 tbsp butter, softened
- Sea salt and black pepper, to taste

1. Brush the chicken with melted butter, coat with salt and black pepper, and arrange in a baking dish. Bake in the oven for 35-40 minutes at 360 F until crispy and browned.
2. In a bowl, mix the rest of the ingredients to form the topping. Serve alongside the prepared chicken.

PER SERVING

Calories: 235 | Fat 21g | Carbs: 1.3g | Protein 5.4g

Moroccan Roast Chicken

Prep time: 5-10 minutes |Cook time: 22 minutes |Serves 4

- 3 tbsp plain yogurt
- 4 skinless, boneless chicken thighs
- 4 garlic cloves, chopped
- 2 tsp ground cumin
- 2 tsp paprika
- ¼ tsp crushed red pepper flakes

1. Take your food processor and add garlic, yogurt, salt, oil and blend as well.
2. Take a mixing bowl and add chicken, red pepper flakes, cumin, parsley, garlic, and mix well.
3. Let it marinate for 2-4 hours.
4. Pre-heat Ninja Foodi by pressing the "ROAST" option and setting it to "400 degrees F" and timer to 23 minutes.
5. Let it pre-heat until you hear a beep.

PER SERVING

Calories: 321| Carbs: 6 g | Protein: 21 g | Fat: 24 g

Thyme Chicken Thighs

Prep time: 30 minutes | Cook time: 8 minutes | Serves 4

- ½ cup chicken stock
- 1 tbsp olive oil
- ½ cup chopped onion
- 4 chicken thighs
- ¼ cup heavy cream
- 2 tbsp Dijon mustard
- 1 tsp thyme
- 1 tsp garlic powder

1. Heat the olive oil in a pan. Cook the chicken for about 4 minutes per side. Set aside. Sauté the onion in the same pan for 3 minutes, add the stock, and simmer for 5 minutes. Stir in mustard and heavy cream, along with thyme and garlic powder.
2. Pour the sauce over the chicken and serve.

PER SERVING

Calories: 528 | Fat: 42g | Carbs: 4g | Protein: 33g

Grilled Huli Huli Chicken

Prep time 5 minutes|Cook time: 12 minutes|- Serves 8

- 6-8 chicken legs
- ½ tsp fresh ginger, minced or crushed
- 1 tsp garlic, minced or crushed
- ¼ cup brown sugar
- 3 tbsp ketchup
- 4 tbsp soy sauce
- 2 tbsp chicken stock, as needed

1. In a bowl, add ketchup, soy sauce, garlic, ginger, and brown sugar. thin up the marinade a bit to make it easier to cover the chicken.
2. In a container or bag add your chicken all over the chicken. Cover and let marinate at least 2 hours to overnight.
3. Remove the Huli Huli chicken from the with your favorite sides.

PER SERVING

Calories: 509 | Carbs: 8g | Protein: 63g | Fat: 23g

Marinated Fried Chicken

Prep time: 20 minutes | Cook time: 3 minutes |Serves 4

- 3 tbsp olive oil
- 4 chicken breasts, cut into strips
- ½ cup pork rinds, crushed
- 8 ounces jarred pickle juice
- 1 egg

1. Cover the chicken with pickle juice, in a bowl, and refrigerate for 12 hours while covered.
2. Whisk the egg in one bowl, and place the pork rinds in a separate one. Dip the chicken pieces in the egg, then in pork rinds. Ensure they are well coated.
3. Set a pan over medium heat and warm oil, fry the chicken for 3 minutes on each side, remove to paper towels, drain the excess grease and serve.

PER SERVING

Calories: 393 | Fat: 15.6g | Carbs: 3.1g | Protein 21.8g

Chapter 10

Seafood Splendor

Codfish Nuggets

Prep time: 15 minutes | Cook time: 10 minutes | Serves 4

- 1 large egg
- ½ cup finely ground almond flour
- ½ cup nutritional yeast flakes
- ½ teaspoon garlic powder
- ½ teaspoon onion powder
- 1 pound cod fillets, cut into bite-size pieces

1. In a large shallow bowl, whisk the egg by hand until foamy. Set aside.
2. In another large shallow bowl, stir together the almond flour, nutritional yeast, garlic powder, onion powder, Old Bay seasoning (if using), salt, and pepper.
3. Line a plate with paper towels. Drain on the paper towels.

PER SERVING

Calories: 249 | Fat: 13g | Carbs: 5g | Protein: 28g

Salmon with Herb Cream Sauce

Prep time: 20 minutes | Cook time: 5 minutes | Serves 2

- 2 salmon fillets
- ¾ tsp dill

Sauce:
- 2 tbsp butter
- ¼ cup heavy cream

1. Season the salmon with dill and tarragon. Melt the duck fat in a pan over medium heat.
2. Add salmon, and cook, for about 4 minutes on both sides. Set aside. Melt the butter and add the dill and tarragon. Serve the salmon topped with the sauce.

PER SERVING

Calories: 468 | Carbs: 1.5g | Fat: 40g | Protein 22g

Grilled Salmon

Prep time: 5 minutes | Cook time: 40 minutes | Serves 6

- 6-ounce salmon fillet, with skin
- sea salt to taste

1. Preheat cast iron pan to medium high heat - if you're not sure, go higher. Preheat for at least 5 minutes. Pat salmon dry and sprinkle with sea salt.
2. Lower thawed fish in and sprinkle with 1/2 teaspoon sea salt. Turn off heat as soon as the fish is in, and cover. Allow to cook in the hot water, covered, for 20-30 minutes. Drain and serve, sprinkling with additional salt if desired.

PER SERVING

Calories: 280| Fat: 15 g | Protein: 36g | Carbs:0 g

Poached Scallops

Prep time: 5 minutes | Cook time: 20 minutes | Serves 4

- ½ cup chicken broth
- ¼ cup water
- 1 tablespoon minced shallots
- ½ teaspoon salt
- 1 pound sea scallops

1. In a medium saucepan, combine the chicken broth, water, shallots, and salt simmer for 5 minutes, or until the shallots are softened.
2. Remove the pan from the heat and allow the scallops to rest in the liquid for 10 minutes to absorb the flavor before serving.

PER SERVING

Calories: 80 | Fat: 1g | Carbs: 4g | Protein: 14g

Bacon-Wrapped Scallops

Prep time: 15 minutes | Cook time: 15 minutes | Serves 4

- 8 large sea scallops
- 4 slices thin bacon (Applegate is thin)

1. Preheat oven to 425°F and line a baking sheet with parchment paper. Cut bacon in half crosswise. Precook bacon for 3–4 minutes flat on the parchment. As the bacon cooks, pat scallops dry with paper towels and set aside.
2. Once bacon has cooled until it's cool enough to touch, wrap bacon around each scallop and secure with a toothpick. Place on baking sheet, and repeat with the remaining scallops. Bake for 12 minutes and then serve warm.

PER SERVING

Calories: 422| Fat: 31g | Protein: 35g | Carbs: 2g

Dill Potted Salmon

Prep time: 15 minutes, plus 2 hours to chill | Cook time: 15 minute| Serves 4

½ pound canned salmon or cooked salmon
½ cup plain low-fat greek yogurt
¼ cup butter, melted
juice and zest from ½ lemon
1 tablespoon finely chopped fresh dill
sea salt, for seasoning
freshly ground black pepper, for seasoning

1. In a medium bowl, mix together the salmon, yogurt, butter, lemon juice, lemon zest, and dill until well combined.
2. Season with salt and pepper.
3. Chill the potted salmon for at least 2 hours before serving.

PER SERVING

Calories: 228 | Fat: 17g |Protein: 18g | Carbs: 2g

Lobster Roll In A Bowl

Prep time: 10 minutes | Cook time: 10 minutes |
Serves 4

- 12 ounces cooked lobster meat, chopped
- 2 tablespoons melted butter
- 1 teaspoon garlic powder
- 4 slices of cooked bacon, chopped
- ¼ cup mayonnaise
- 1 teaspoon lemon zest
- Juice of ½ lemon
- 1 scallion, thinly sliced
- Pinch salt
- Pinch freshly ground black pepper

1. Preheat the oven to 300°F.
2. Brush the cooked bacon with the melted butter, and season with garlic powder. Remove from the oven and set aside.
3. Divide the lobster and bacon mixture among four bowls. Top with the toasted bacon pieces and serve immediately.

PER SERVING

Calories: 470 | Fat: 33g| Carbs:0 g | Protein: 28g

Broiled Honey Sesame Shrimp

Prep time: 5 minutes | Cook time: 10 minutes |
Serves 4

- ¼ cup honey
- 2 teaspoons minced garlic
- 2 teaspoons grated fresh ginger
- 1 teaspoon sesame oil
- sea salt, for seasoning
- freshly ground black pepper, for seasoning
- 1 pound shrimp, peeled and deveined
- 1 scallion, thinly sliced on the bias

1. Preheat the oven to 450°F. Line a 9-by-13-inch baking dish with parchment paper and set aside.
2. In a medium bowl, stir together the honey, garlic, ginger, and sesame oil.
3. Season the mixture with salt and pepper.
4. Serve topped with the scallion.

PER SERVING

Calories: 181 | Fat: 2g | Protein: 23g | Carbs: 19g

Garlic-and-Herb-Roasted Sardines

Prep time: 5 minutes | Cook time: 20 minutes | Serves 4

- 1 pound fresh sardines
- 2 teaspoons garlic powder
- 1 tablespoon dried oregano
- ½ teaspoon freshly ground black pepper
- 5 tablespoons salted butter, melted

1. Preheat the oven to 425°F. Line a baking sheet with aluminum foil.
2. Clean the sardines and rinse them well; then pat them dry.
3. Transfer the roasted sardines to a plate and serve warm or store in an airtight container in the refrigerator for up to 2 days.

PER SERVING

Calories: 356 | Fat: 30g | Carbs: 2g | Protein: 19g

Crispy Baked Fish Sticks

Prep time: 10 minutes | Cook time: 8 minutes | Serves 4

- Melted lard or tallow, for greasing the air fryer
- 1 large egg
- 1 cup powdered Parmesan cheese or pork dust (for dairy-free)
- Bacon Mayonnaise, for serving (optional)

1. Preheat the oven or an air fryer to 400°F. If using the oven, line a rimmed baking sheet with parchment paper. If using an air fryer, grease the air fryer basket with melted lard.
2. Transfer the fish sticks to a platter and serve with mayonnaise, if desired fryer for about 3 minutes, or until heated through.

PER SERVING

Calories: 194 | Fat: 10 g | Protein: 22 g | Carbs: 0.1 g

Appendix 1 Measurement Conversion Chart

Volume Equivalents (Dry)

US STANDARD	METRIC (APPROXIMATE)
1/8 teaspoon	0.5 mL
1/4 teaspoon	1 mL
1/2 teaspoon	2 mL
3/4 teaspoon	4 mL
1 teaspoon	5 mL
1 tablespoon	15 mL
1/4 cup	59 mL
1/2 cup	118 mL
3/4 cup	177 mL
1 cup	235 mL
2 cups	475 mL
3 cups	700 mL
4 cups	1 L

Volume Equivalents (Liquid)

US STANDARD	US STANDARD (OUNCES)	METRIC (APPROXIMATE)
2 tablespoons	1 fl.oz.	30 mL
1/4 cup	2 fl.oz.	60 mL
1/2 cup	4 fl.oz.	120 mL
1 cup	8 fl.oz.	240 mL
1 1/2 cup	12 fl.oz.	355 mL
2 cups or 1 pint	16 fl.oz.	475 mL
4 cups or 1 quart	32 fl.oz.	1 L
1 gallon	128 fl.oz.	4 L

Temperatures Equivalents

FAHRENHEIT(F)	CELSIUS(C) APPROXIMATE)
225 °F	107 °C
250 °F	120 ° °C
275 °F	135 °C
300 °F	150 °C
325 °F	160 °C
350 °F	180 °C
375 °F	190 °C
400 °F	205 °C
425 °F	220 °C
450 °F	235 °C
475 °F	245 °C
500 °F	260 °C

Weight Equivalents

US STANDARD	METRIC (APPROXIMATE)
1 ounce	28 g
2 ounces	57 g
5 ounces	142 g
10 ounces	284 g
15 ounces	425 g
16 ounces (1 pound)	455 g
1.5 pounds	680 g
2 pounds	907 g

Appendix 2 The Dirty Dozen and Clean Fifteen

The Environmental Working Group (EWG) is a nonprofit, nonpartisan organization dedicated to protecting human health and the environment Its mission is to empower people to live healthier lives in a healthier environment. This organization publishes an annual list of the twelve kinds of produce, in sequence, that have the highest amount of pesticide residue-the Dirty Dozen-as well as a list of the fifteen kinds ofproduce that have the least amount of pesticide residue-the Clean Fifteen.

THE DIRTY DOZEN	
The 2016 Dirty Dozen includes the following produce. These are considered among the year's most important produce to buy organic:	
Strawberries	Spinach
Apples	Tomatoes
Nectarines	Bell peppers
Peaches	Cherry tomatoes
Celery	Cucumbers
Grapes	Kale/collard greens
Cherries	Hot peppers
The Dirty Dozen list contains two additional itemskale/collard greens and hot peppers- because they tend to contain trace levels of highly hazardous pesticides.	

THE CLEAN FIFTEEN	
The least critical to buy organically are the Clean Fifteen list. The following are on the 2016 list:	
Avocados	Papayas
Corn	Kiw
Pineapples	Eggplant
Cabbage	Honeydew
Sweet peas	Grapefruit
Onions	Cantaloupe
Asparagus	Cauliflower
Mangos	
Some of the sweet corn sold in the United States are made from genetically engineered (GE) seedstock. Buy organic varieties of these crops to avoid GE produce.	

Appendix 3 Index

A

almond flour 30, 57
anchovies 38

B

bacon 22, 24, 26, 29, 31, 37, 47, 50, 52, 59, 60
balsamic vinegar 37, 48
basil 18, 23, 31, 35, 44, 48
basil leaves 35, 44
beef heart 36, 44
Beef Stock 16, 43
black pepper 24, 25, 26, 28, 29, 30, 41, 43
brisket 41
brown sugar 29, 42, 49, 55
butter 17, 19, 20, 22, 24, 25, 30, 38, 48, 53, 57, 59

C

camembert cheese 31
Carnivore Hollandaise 22
cayenne pepper 23, 29, 35, 43
Ceylon cinnamon 34
cheddar cheese 24, 43, 50
Cheesecloth 19
chicken 17, 20, 30, 32, 34, 35, 38, 52, 53, 54, 55, 58
chicken feet 20
chorizo 25
cornstarch 43
cumin 16, 18, 54

D

dried basil 18

E

dried dill 28
dried oregano 18, 35, 61
drumsticks 17

E

eggs 15, 17, 22, 23, 24, 25, 26, 28, 36, 50
egg yolks 19

F

feta cheese 22, 40, 52
fine sea salt 15, 19, 23, 34, 40, 45, 47, 52
fresh basil leaves 35
fresh ginger 19, 49, 55, 60
fresh parsley 20

G

garlic powder 28, 30, 32, 35, 36, 41, 54, 57
ground beef 28, 40, 43, 44

H

ham hocks 23
heavy cream 17, 20, 50, 54, 57
honey 19, 32, 34, 42
hot sauce 30, 32, 35, 37, 48, 53

K

ketchup 55
kosher salt 41, 47

L

lamb loin chops 45

lemon 16, 18, 36, 37, 42, 45, 49, 59, 60

lemon zest 36, 59, 60

lime juice 29

M

macadamia nuts 44

maple syrup 29

marrow bones 16

mayonnaise 28, 29, 37, 60, 61

monkfish 37

mozzarella cheese 25, 48

mustard powder 28

N

nutritional yeast 57

nuts 44

O

olive oil 16, 18, 25, 36, 43, 45, 53, 54, 55

onion powder 28, 41, 57

oregano 18, 35, 36, 45, 48, 61

P

paprika 28, 31, 54

Parmesan cheese 31, 35, 61

patties 25, 40, 43, 50

pesto 31

pork rinds 15, 35, 50, 55

pork sausage 15

R

Ranch seasoning mix 37

red onions 23, 35, 48, 58, 59

roast beef 22

rosemary sprig 41, 45, 50, 56

S

salt 15, 16, 17, 18, 19, 20, 23, 24, 25, 26, 28, 30, 32, 34, 36, 37, 40, 41, 42, 43, 44, 45, 47, 48

salted butter 22, 24, 38, 61

serrano pepper 23, 48, 54, 59

shallot 36

Short Ribs 43, 48, 50, 58

soy sauce 47, 49, 55

Swiss cheese 26

T

tallow 22, 23, 38, 40, 47, 49, 52, 61

thyme 34, 41, 45, 48, 54

W

Worcestershire sauce 53

Y

yellow mustard 43, 48

yogurt 29, 54, 59

Jessica G. Snider